Piano Exam Pieces

ABRSM Grade 3

Selected from the 2021 & 2022 syllabus

Name

Date of exam

C000292364

Contents

page

Editor for ABRSM: Richard Jones

Other pieces for Grade 3

Published in 2020 by ABRSM (Publishing) Ltd, a wholly owned subsidiary of ABRSM, 4 London Wall Place, London EC2Y 5AU, United Kingdom

© 2020 by The Associated Board of the Royal Schools of Music

Distributed worldwide by Oxford University Press

Music origination by Julia Bovee

Cover by Kate Benjamin & Andy Potts, with thanks to Brighton College

Printed in England by Halstan & Co. Ltd, Amersham, Bucks., on materials from sustainable sources.

P15179

Ecossaise in E flat

No. 4 from *Six Ecossaises*, WoO 83

Ludwig van Beethoven
(1770–1827)

The écossaise is a dance in a lively 2/4 time. Its name is French for 'Scottish', and it might have originated in Scotland. It became very popular in Vienna in the early 19th century, and sets of écossaises were composed by both Beethoven and Schubert. Beethoven's *Six Ecossaises* (WoO 83) date from about 1806.

Source: first edition, Beethoven: *Gesamtausgabe*, Series 25, No. 44 (Leipzig: Breitkopf & Härtel, 1888). The *f* in bar 17 is original; all other dynamics are editorial suggestions only. Additional slurs have also been supplied by the editor.

A:2

Innocence

No. 5 from *25 études faciles et progressives*, Op. 100

J. F. F. Burgmüller
(1806–74)

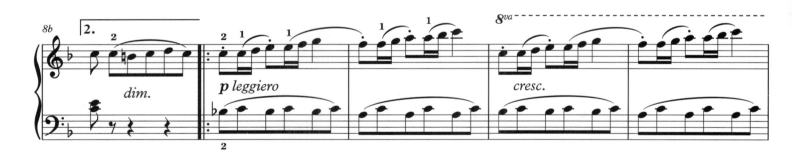

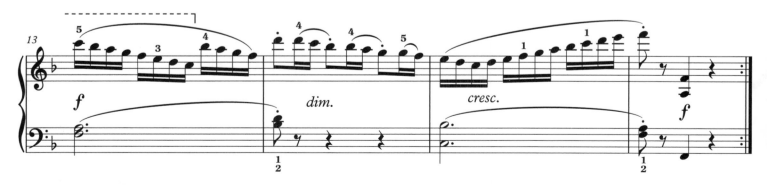

Johann Friedrich Franz Burgmüller, German by birth, settled in Paris after 1832. He became popular there as a pianist and composer, improvising hundreds of salon pieces and composing much piano music for teaching purposes. Many of his short piano pieces, like this one, have programmatic titles.

Source: *25 études faciles et progressives*, Op. 100 (London: Schott, 1854)

Gavotte in G

HWV 491

G. F. Handel
(1685–1759)

This is one of George Frideric Handel's earliest keyboard pieces, composed around 1705 when he was only 20 and living in the north German city of Hamburg. There he played violin, and later harpsichord, in the Hamburg Opera. At that time, too, he composed keyboard pieces, arias, cantatas and his first opera, *Almira*.

The gavotte is a graceful Baroque dance movement, usually moderate in tempo. Handel's themes give it a lyrical character: a three-note figure (first falling, then rising) in bar 1; and a sequence of two-note slurred figures in bars 2–3. Almost the whole piece is based on these two themes.

Source: MS copy, London, British Library, R.M. 19.a.4. The slurs in bar 3 are editorial suggestions only, as are all the dynamics and ornaments.

Adapted from *Baroque Keyboard Pieces*, Book I, edited by Richard Jones (ABRSM)

Love's Greeting

Salut d'amour

Op. 12

Arranged by Richard Jones

Edward Elgar
(1857–1934)

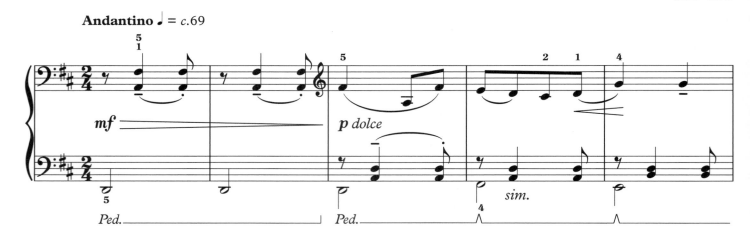

The English composer Edward Elgar was born and brought up in Worcester, and although he periodically lived and worked in London, he always returned to the counties that he knew and loved, Worcestershire and Herefordshire. Mainly self-taught as a composer, he became famous throughout Europe following the first performances of the 'Enigma' Variations (1899) and *The Dream of Gerontius* (1900).

Since Elgar was a fine violinist, it is hardly surprising that some of his best-loved pieces are for violin and piano, notably the *Chanson de matin* (Morning Song) (1899) and *Salut d'amour* (Love's Greeting), written in 1888. They are often arranged for other instruments, including this new arrangement for solo piano.

B:2

Andante

from Trumpet Concerto in E flat, Hob. VIIe:1, second movement

Arranged by Martin White

Joseph Haydn
(1732–1809)

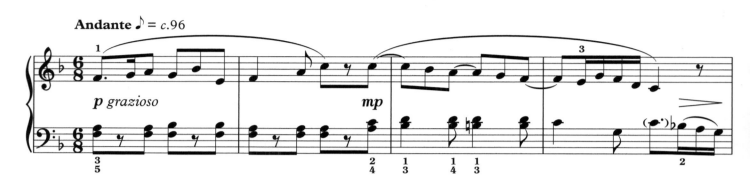

This is a piano arrangement of the slow movement from Haydn's Trumpet Concerto in E flat (Hob. VIIe:1), which was composed in 1796 when he was working in Vienna (1795–1809). It was written for the new keyed trumpet, which made pitches available that were missing on the old natural trumpet at that time. The slow movement illustrates the lyrical, melodious style that is often found in Haydn's late works.

Anastasia

from *It's a Piano Thing*, Book 2

B:3

Ailbhe McDonagh
(born 1982)

Ailbhe McDonagh is an Irish cellist and composer. She is a graduate of the Eastman School of Music in Rochester NY, USA, and of the Royal Irish Academy of Music in Dublin, Ireland, where she has taught the cello since 2010.

  She has published two books of piano pieces under the title *It's a Piano Thing*. 'Anastasia' is taken from the second book. The composer has written of this piece: 'Aim for a beautiful singing *legato* sound in the right hand; think of the long phrases and try not to allow any interruption. The lower voice is the more important of the two in the left hand; so, to create the correct balance in sound, ensure that the inner voice is always softer than the right hand and the lower voice.'

Disco Baroque

C:1

Alan Bullard
(born 1947)

The British composer Alan Bullard is particularly well known for his choral and educational music. He studied with Herbert Howells at the Royal College of Music in London and later taught at the Colchester Institute for 30 years (1975–2005).

Bullard says of this piece: 'Disco dominated popular music during the late 1970s. Using similar sequences to those found in earlier music, this piece suggests the rhythmic disco feel with a steady drum beat, which should be maintained (in your head!) in the middle section.' The piece is taken from *Piano Time Dance*, edited by Pauline Hall (OUP).

верхом на палочке Verkhom na palochke

Riding the Hobby-Horse

No. 5 from *Children's Album*, Op. 98

C:2

A. T. Grechaninov
(1864–1956)

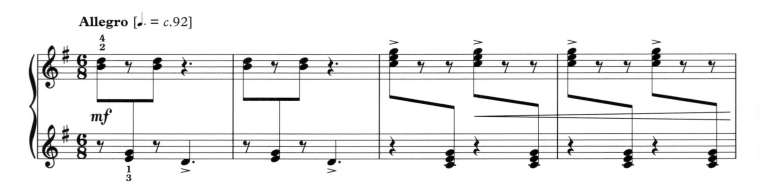

The Russian composer Aleksandr Tikhonovich Grechaninov studied at the Moscow and St Petersburg Conservatories. He then taught in these two Russian cities before moving to Paris in 1925. When the Second World War broke out in 1939, he emigrated to the USA, becoming an American citizen in 1946. His large output includes piano music, songs, operas, and five symphonies. His *Children's Album* (Детский альбом Detskiy al'bom) dates from 1924. This piece describes a ride on a hobby-horse, and in the last ten bars the composer comments on the progress of the journey: 'Too far' (bar 19) and 'All's well that ends well' (bar 23).

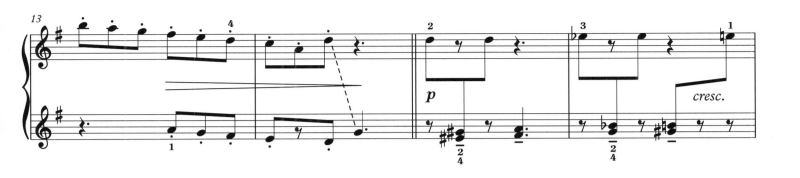

Too far

All's well that ends well

Scary Stuff

from *Razzamajazz Repertoire Piano*

Sarah Watts

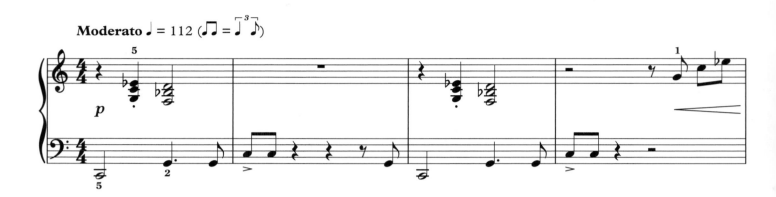

Sarah Watts studied bassoon and piano at the Royal College of Music in London. At an early age she was inspired by her mother, who played jazz at home and encouraged her to improvise. One of her main musical activities today is composition. As well as writing piano music, she has published musicals, choral works, and several books of educational music, including the *Razzamajazz* series. In bar 20 of this piece, she asks for *tremolo*, a rapid alternation of the notes of the chord. The composer says: '"Scary Stuff" is a cool, laid-back swing piece. It should feel at first as if you are quietly creeping into a spooky place. As you continue there are a few tense moments where things might be getting a bit scary. At bar 20 "something" happens and there is a loud scream. Thankfully things calm down after that and you are able to creep out of the place. All is well!'